TRINITY
COLLEGE LONDON

Electronic Keyboard
Grade 5

Pieces & Technical Work
for Trinity College London exams

2015-2018

Published by:
Trinity College London
www.trinitycollege.com

Registered in England
Company no. 02683033
Charity no. 1014792

Printed in England by Caligraving Ltd.

Impromptu in A♭

D. 935 no. 2

Franz Schubert
arr. Andrew Smith

Voices:	Jazz Guitar, Vibes
Style:	Jazz Waltz

PLEASE SET UP FOR THE NEXT PIECE

Radetzky March

Johann Strauss Snr.
arr. Victoria Proudler

Voices:	Horns, Marcato Strings, Orchestral, Piccolo (sounding octave higher)
Style:	March

Paragon Rag

Scott Joplin
arr. Nancy Litten

PLEASE SET UP FOR THE NEXT PIECE

Entry of the Gladiators

Julius Fučík
arr. Rory Marsden

Voices: Brass Section, Horns, Strings, Trombone, Xylophone
Style: March

Puttin' on the Ritz

Irving Berlin

arr. Jeremy Ward

Voice:

Style:

* Candidates should refer to the current syllabus requirements for Own Interpretation pieces.

PLEASE SET UP FOR THE NEXT PIECE

Georgia on my Mind

Hoagy Carmichael/Stuart Gorrell
arr. Andrew Smith

Voices: Harmonica, Strings, Tenor Sax (sounding octave lower), Vibes
Style: Swing

PLEASE SET UP FOR THE NEXT PIECE

Waltz

from *Masquerade*

Aram Khachaturian
arr. Joanna Clarke

Voices: Flute, Horn, Strings
Style: Viennese Waltz

The repeat must be played in the exam.

Twilight Tango

Victoria Proudler

Voices: Flute, Piano, Violin
Style: Tango

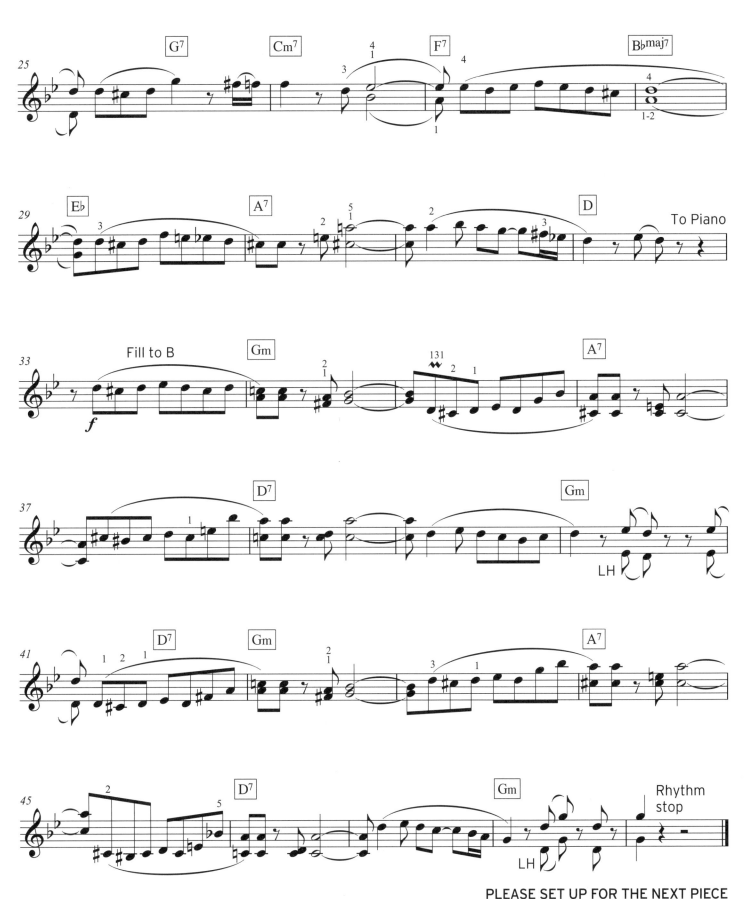

PLEASE SET UP FOR THE NEXT PIECE

Birdland

Joe Zawinul
arr. Joanna Clarke

Voices:	Bass, Brass, Saxophone, Synth
Style:	Disco

The repeats must be played in the exam.

PLEASE SET UP FOR THE NEXT PIECE

Water Pistols at Dawn

Nancy Litten

Voices: Musette Accordion, Mandolin, Synth, Pad
Style: Tango

PLEASE SET UP FOR THE NEXT PIECE

Technical Work

Technical work – candidates to prepare in full *either* section i) *or* section ii)					
either **i) Scales & chord knowledge** (from memory) – the examiner will select from the following:					
D♭ and B major B♭ and G♯ minor (candidate's choice of either harmonic *or* melodic *or* natural minor) Chromatic scales in similar motion starting on D♭ and B G harmonic minor contrary motion scale	min. ♩ = 110	two octaves	*legato* and *mf*	hands together, unless otherwise stated	piano voice with auto-accompaniment off
Blues scale starting on F and A (straight *and* swung rhythm)				R.H. only	
Chords of D♭^{maj7}, B^{maj7}, B♭m^7, G♯m^7, B♭m^{maj7}, G♯m^{maj7}, D♭^{6}, B^6, B♭m^6, G♯m^6 Perfect cadence in C, G and F major				bass note in the left hand and three notes of the chord in the right hand	
or **ii) Exercises** (music may be used):					
Candidates to prepare **all** three exercises. The candidate will choose one exercise to play first; the examiner will then select one of the remaining two exercises to be performed.					
Cool Beans			keyboard functions exercise		
Rock Amok			scalic exercise		
Balancing Act			pianistic exercise		

Please refer to the current syllabus for details on all elements of the exam

i) Scales & chord knowledge

Db major scale (two octaves)

B major scale (two octaves)

Bb minor scale: harmonic (two octaves)

Bb minor scale: melodic (two octaves)

Bb minor scale: natural (two octaves)

G# minor scale: harmonic (two octaves)

G# minor scale: melodic (two octaves)

G# minor scale: natural (two octaves)

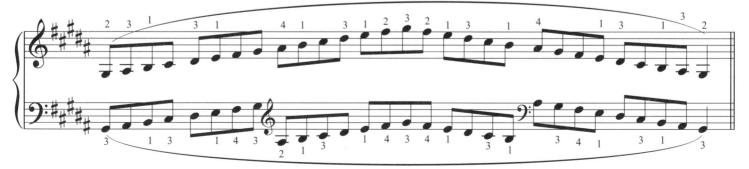

G harmonic minor contrary motion scale (two octaves)

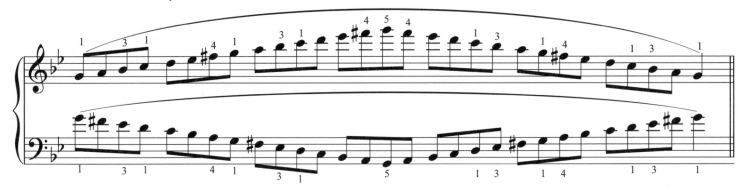

Chromatic scale in similar motion starting on D♭ (two octaves)

Chromatic scale in similar motion starting on B (two octaves)

Blues scale starting on F (two octaves), straight *and* swung rhythm

Right hand

Blues scale starting on A (two octaves), straight *and* swung rhythm

Right hand

Db^maj7

B^maj7

Bbm^7

G#m^7

Bbm^maj7

G#m^maj7

please turn over

Db⁶

B⁶

Bbm⁶

G#m⁶

Perfect cadence in C major

Perfect cadence in G major

Perfect cadence in F major

ii) Exercises

1. Cool Beans – keyboard functions exercise

Voices:	Clavichord, Wah Clavi.
Style:	Jazz Funk

please turn over

2. Rock Amok – scalic exercise

Voice:	Lead Guitar (sounding octave lower)
Style:	Hard Rock

3. Balancing Act – pianistic exercise

Voice:	Electric Piano
Style:	None